ALL THIS AND SNOOPY, TOO

Selected Cartoons from
YOU CAN'T WIN, CHARLIE BROWN
VOL 1

By CHARLES M. SCHULZ

A FAWCETT CREST BOOK
Fawcett Publications, Inc., Greenwich, Conn.

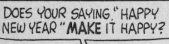

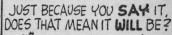

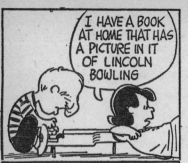

AMAZING!

THEY'VE FINALLY DEVELOPED
A BONELESS CAT!

DEAR PENCIL PAL,
I HAVE ALWAYS KNOWN IT WASN'T PROPER FOR ME TO WRITE TO YOU WITH PENCIL.

THEREFORE, TODAY I AM GOING TO TRY AGAIN TO WRITE TO YOU WITH

SIGH

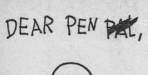

IT ALWAYS SEEMS SO QUIET AROUND HERE ON THE DAY HE GOES TO VISIT HIS GRANDFATHER...

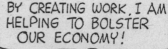

ALL OF EARTH'S CREATURES HAVE, HIDDEN WITHIN THEIR BEINGS, A WILD UNCONTROLLABLE URGE TO **PUNT** !

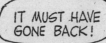

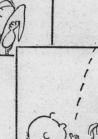

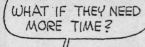

WHEN YOU'RE ON YOUR WAY TO SCHOOL, AND YOU MEET A DOG, YOU SHOULD ALWAYS STOP, AND PAT HIM ON THE HEAD...

PAT PAT

THAT ALWAYS GETS YOUR DAY OFF TO A GOOD START..

WELL, AT LEAST I'M CONTRIBUTING **SOMETHING** TO SOCIETY!

GOOD GRIEF! HERE COMES LUCY! I'M TRAPPED!

SHE SAID SHE'D THROW MY BLANKET IN THE TRASH BURNER THE NEXT TIME SHE SAW IT....

WHAT DOES MISS OTHMAR THINK ABOUT YOUR BRINGING THAT BLANKET TO SCHOOL?

SHE DOESN'T LIKE IT SO I'M TRYING TO GET HER TO MAKE AN AGREEMENT WITH ME...

I TOLD HER I'D GIVE UP MY BLANKET IF SHE'D GIVE UP BITING HER FINGERNAILS...

WHAT DID SHE SAY TO THAT?

I COULDN'T TELL... SHE HAD HER HEAD DOWN ON THE DESK!

WHAT A SITUATION..

MISS OTHMAR IS GOING TO PROVE TO LINUS THAT YOU CAN BREAK A HABIT WITH SHEER WILL POWER SO SHE'S GOING TO STOP BITING HER FINGERNAILS

LINUS IS SO SURE THAT SHE CAN'T DO IT HE'S RISKING HIS BELOVED BLANKET..

IN THESE TEACHER-PUPIL STRUGGLES IT'S ALWAYS THE PRINCIPAL WHO LOSES!

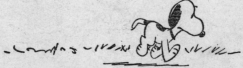

YOU CAN'T HEAR
WORMS THIS TIME OF
YEAR...THE GROUND
IS TOO HARD..

I DIDN'T
REALIZE
"WORM-LISTENING"
WAS SO
SEASONAL!

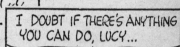

I PROMISED CHARLIE BROWN THAT I'D TRY TO TALK TO YOU, SCHROEDER..

NOW, LET'S BE PRACTICAL ABOUT THIS THING..WHO MAKES THE MOST MONEY, A CONCERT PIANIST OR A BASEBALL CATCHER?

A CONCERT PIANIST!

WHAT'S THE MATTER WITH YOU, CHARLIE BROWN? WHY DON'T YOU LEAVE SCHROEDER ALONE?!

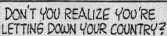

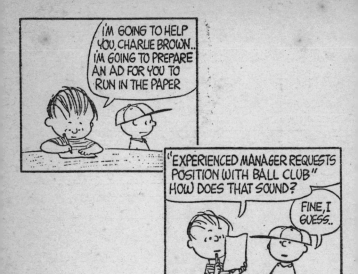